SIT THE F*CK DOWN AND COLOR

ADULT SWEAR WORD COLORING BOOK FOR STRESS RELIEF

Free Stuff?
Yes Please!

Like free stuff? So do we! Come check out the site and get yourself some freebies!

www.swearwordcoloringbooks.com/extra

I take great pride in my art, but even more pride expanding your dictionary into new lands of depravity. However, please keep these new words from children....they are our future for fucks sake!!! This book may not be for kids, but it'll certainly tug at your inner child. Coloring puts a big smile on my face, but colouring the word assbag makes me laugh out loud. I hope you will too.

Now Sit the F*ck Down and Color.

JACKASS

TWAT
WAFFLE

Stank
Dick

Slut
Muffin

SHRIMP
DICK

Ballsack

Schlong

Bitch

BITCHASS

Cuntface

BONER

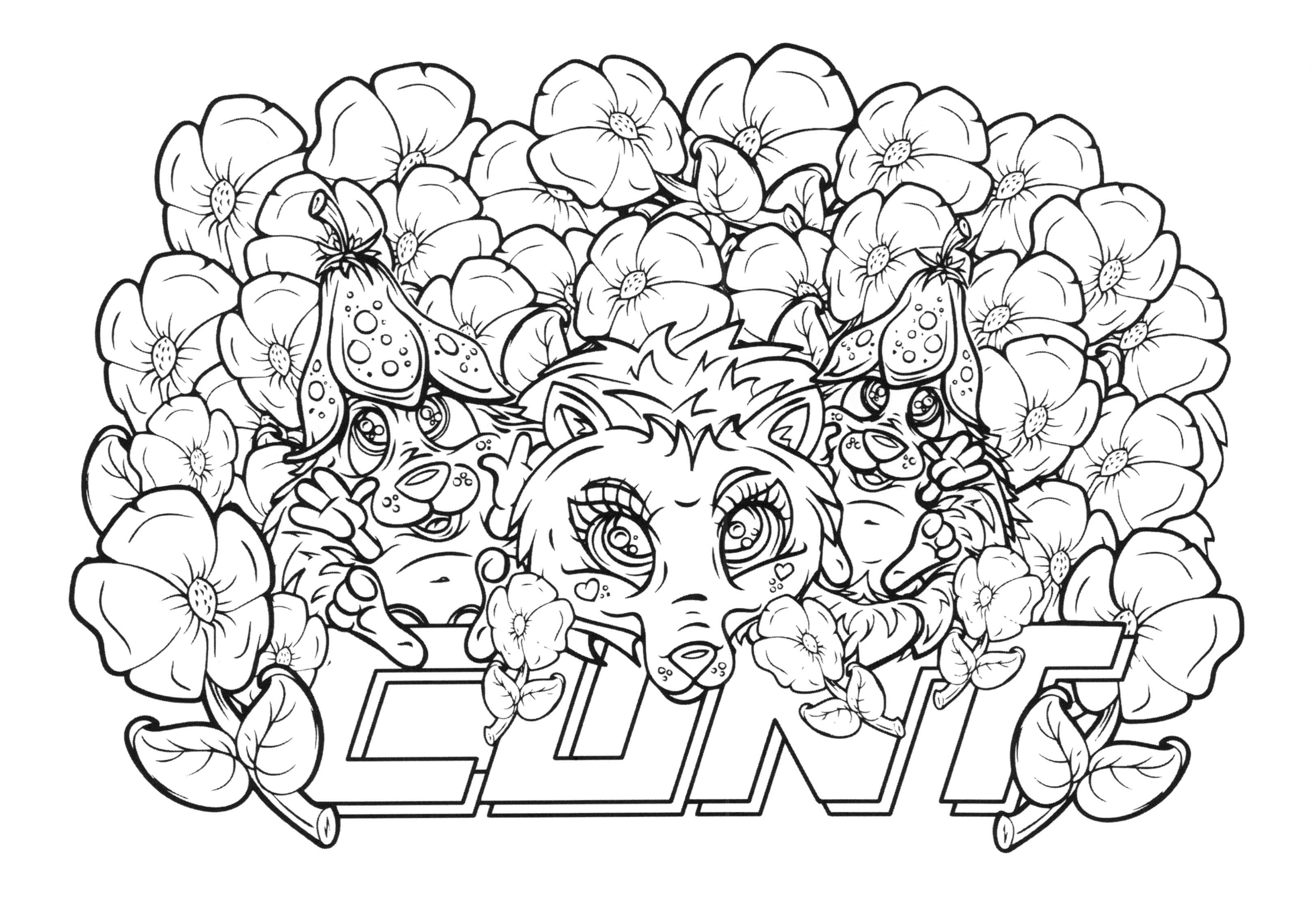
CUNT

Cum Guzzler

Cock
Knocker

DICK
CHEESE

Fuck

Dick
face

ASS
muncher

Dickhead

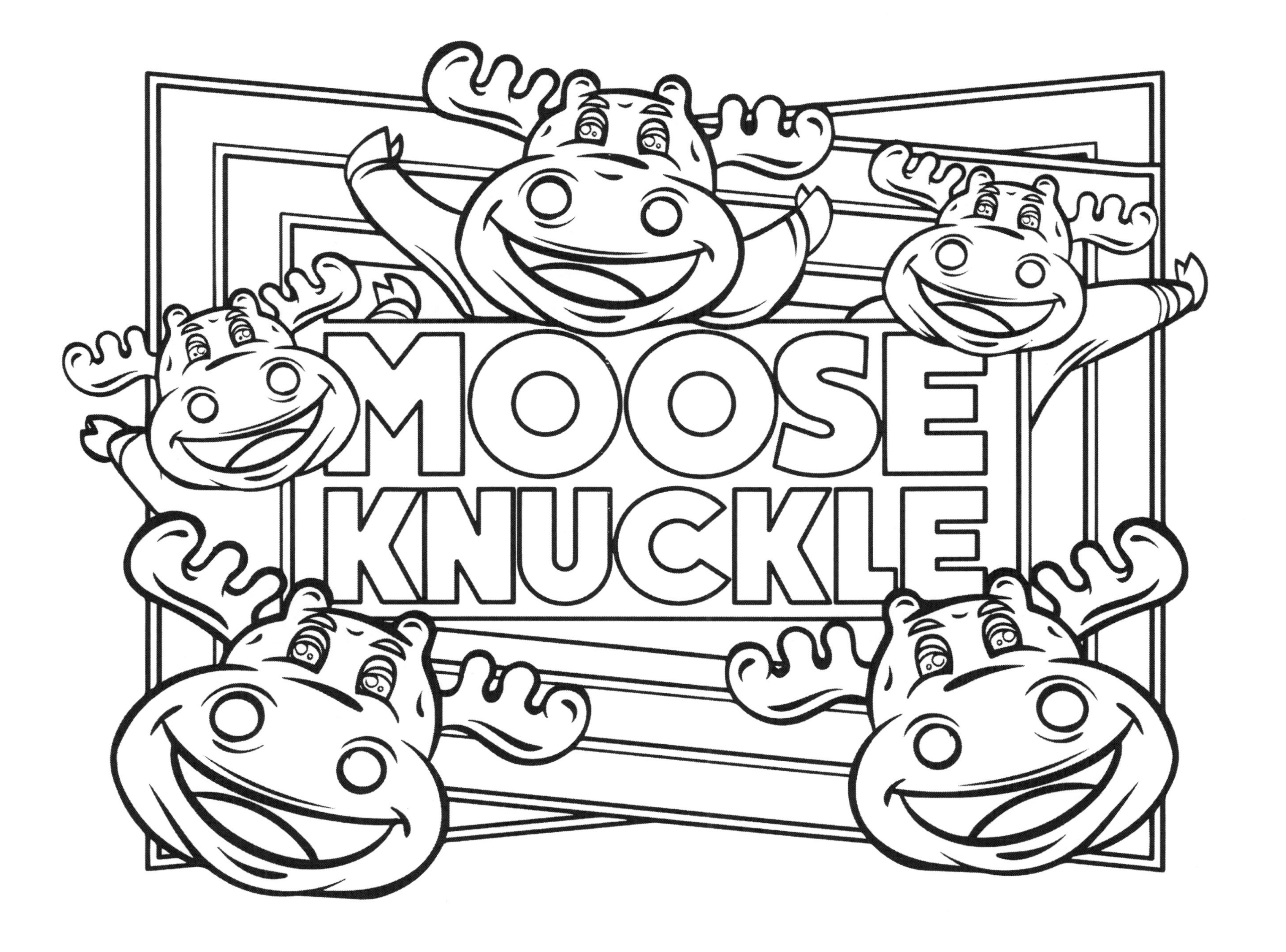
MOOSE
KNUCKLE

LARD

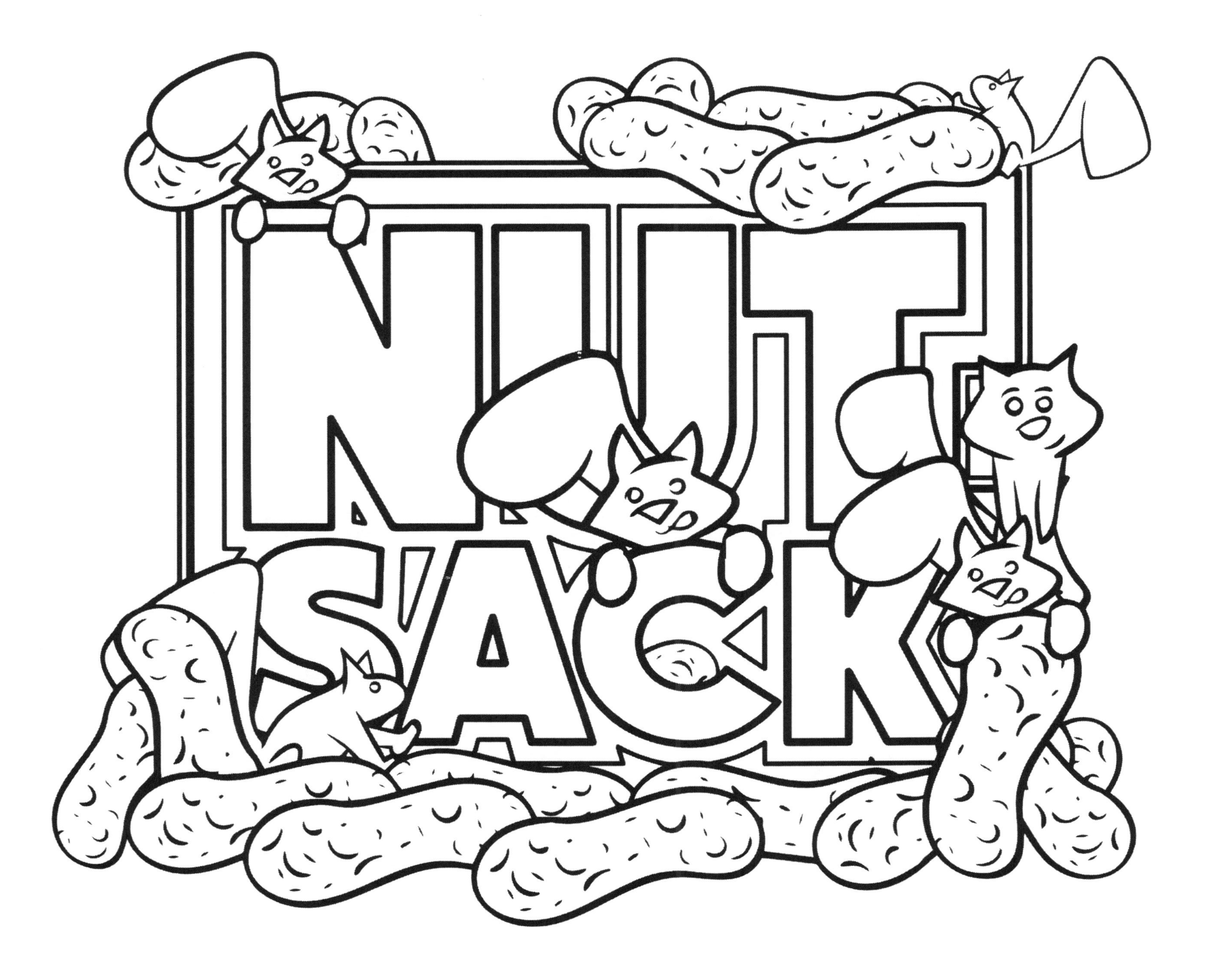
NUT
SACK

Fuckface

THUNDERCUNT

CHUZZLE
FUCKS

Made in the USA
San Bernardino, CA
27 May 2016